BASIC RULES
OF
ENGLISH
GRAMMAR

BOOK 3

Folens
Publishers

	Beginning	Book 1	Book 2	Book 3	Book 4
Adjectives and descriptions	35, 36, 40	29, 30, 31, 34, 41, 48	29, 30, 31, 34	11, 12, 13, 14, 15, 18	11, 13, 18
Adverbs			41, 48	22, 23, 26	15, 16, 18
Alphabet	44, 45	44, 45, 46, 48	27, 28, 34	38, 40	17, 18
Antonyms (opposites)	37		35, 36, 40, 48	16, 18	
Apostrophes				24, 25, 26, 46, 48	22, 26, 46
Capital letters		6, 7, 8, 10	6, 10	27, 34, 46, 48	7, 46, 48
Classification/Sorting	33, 34		37, 40		23,26
Colloquialisms					29, 34
Commas		35, 40	39	45, 48	20, 21, 26
Conjunctions		14, 18	42, 48	37, 40	25, 26
Exclamation marks				31, 34	32
Full stops		6, 7	5, 6, 10	46, 48	19, 46
Homonyms/Homophones/ Commonly confused words		42, 48	38, 40	35, 36, 40	24, 41, 48
Instructions/Information				44	37, 39, 40
Nouns		13, 15			
common	4, 5, 8, 9, 10	16, 17, 18, 19, 20, 21, 25, 26, 37, 40	11, 12, 18	4, 6, 10	4, 10, 42
proper		23, 24, 25, 26	13, 14, 18	4, 10, 27	4, 10
collective					5, 6, 10
Paragraphs					38
Prefixes/Suffixes			46	41, 42, 48	43, 44, 45, 46, 48
Prepositions	14, 15, 16, 17, 18	36, 40	43	39, 40	
Pronouns			16, 18	7, 10	9, 10
Questions/Answers	19, 20, 21, 22, 23, 26	32, 33, 34	24, 25, 26	28, 31, 32, 34	31, 33
Rhyme	46, 48	43, 48		33, 34	
Sentences/Sequencing	6, 7, 10, 11, 12, 13, 18, 24, 25, 27, 28, 30, 31, 32, 34	4, 5, 6, 7, 9, 10, 11	4, 7, 8, 9, 10	17, 44, 47	12, 35, 36, 37, 39, 40
Similes				9, 10	23, 28, 34
Singular/Plural	29, 34	22, 26	15, 18	5	8, 10
Speech/Dialogue		47, 48	32, 33, 34	29, 30, 32, 34	30, 31, 32, 33, 34
Syllabication			44, 45, 48	43, 48	47, 48
Synonyms			47, 48	8	27
Verbs/Root words in verbs	38, 39, 40, 41, 42, 43, 48	34	17, 19, 20, 21, 22, 23, 26	19, 20	42, 48
Verb tenses			20, 26	21, 26	14, 18
Vowels	47, 48	12, 13			

Contents

Editors: Alison Millar and Alison MacTier   Cover image: Barrie Richardson
Layout artist: Suzanne Ward   Cover design: Kim Ashby and Design for Marketing, Ware

© 1996 Folens Limited, on behalf of the authors.
Every effort has been made to contact copyright holders of material used in this book. If any have been overlooked, we will be pleased to make any necessary arrangements.

British Library in Publication Data. A catalogue record for this book is available from the British Library.

First published 1996 by Folens Limited, Dunstable and Dublin.
Folens Limited, Albert House, Apex Business Centre, Boscombe Road, Dunstable, LU5 4RL, England.
Reprinted 1997, 1998, 2000.

ISBN 1 85276234–9

Nouns

Nouns are **naming** words.
Common nouns are **names of things**, like tables or cats.
Proper nouns are **names of people or places**, like Robin Hood or Nottingham.
Proper nouns have **capital letters**.

Example: The **Queen** went to
Dublin in a **car**.

A There are 16 **nouns** in this story. List them.

One windy day, a bird flew out from its nest on the cliffs near Dover.
Some people had left the remains of a picnic on the beach. The bird
swooped and picked up bits of bun, crisps and cake, and flew off with
a sandwich for its dinner.

B Copy and complete the **names** of these countries:

1. ☐ rance   2. ☐ nya

3. ☐ anada   4. ☐ way

5. ☐ gypt   6. ☐ ain

7. ☐ reece   8. ☐ aly

9. ☐ rmany   10. ☐ dia

11. ☐ xico   12. ☐ nited ☐ tates of ☐ ica

An atlas may help.

C The answers to these puzzles are **common nouns**.
See if you can work them out.

1. Its first letter buzzes, its second is in dog but not dig
   and its third is a cross.
2. It rhymes with daughter and is wet.
3. Seven days make one.
4. This fruit sounds like a couple.
5. This word means jump and is a season.
6. This flower rhymes with lazy.
7. It is smaller than you at midday and bigger than you late in the
   afternoon.
8. It is part of a window that sounds sore.

Basic Rules of Grammar: Book 3

Singular and plural

Most nouns can be **singular** or **plural**.
Singular means **one**, plural means **more than one**.

A Copy this chart and complete it with ten of your own examples:

Singular	Plural
tree	trees
house	houses

When you have finished this page, look at your chart again.
Correct any mistakes.

Most **plurals** are formed by adding **s**. Example: the **plural** of tree is trees.
Some **plurals** add other letters. Some **plurals** are the same as the **singular**.

B Write the **plurals** of these words:

child
mouse
foot
tooth

sheep
woman
goose
ox

y/ies plurals

If a word ends in a vowel then **y**, add **s**.

Example: days

If a word ends in a consonant then **y**, change the **y** to **ies**.

Example: ladies.

C Write the **plurals** of these words:

dictionary
balcony
fly
chimney
industry

donkey
ceremony
baby
story
lorry

Masculine and feminine nouns

Man is **masculine**   Woman is **feminine**
Girl is **feminine**   Boy is **masculine**

A Match the **masculine** nouns to the **feminine** nouns in the two lists.
Write the answers like this: prince – princess

god

prince	spinster
son	goddess
lord	niece
master	countess
nephew	bride
sir	madam
bachelor	princess
count	lady
groom	daughter
god	mistress

goddess

B 1. Sort these words into two lists, one for **masculine** and one for **feminine**:

manageress   Mr
actor   queen
Ms   uncle
king   mother
sister   manager
actress   brother
aunt   father

2. Draw lines to link the matching
pairs in your lists.

Pronouns

A **pronoun** is a word used instead of a **noun**.

Example: Tell **Rosie** that the doctor will see **her** now.

Her is a **pronoun** used instead of the **noun Rosie**.

it	her	she	he	I	you	him	me	we	us

A Choose a **pronoun** from the box for each space in this story:

Two Old Friends

Sue met her old friend Carlo. _____ had not seen _____ for a

while, but _____ had not changed much.

"Tell _____ what _____ have been doing," _____

said.

"Well, _____ was at school in Italy," _____ said, "because

my family went there. _____ all enjoyed it."

"_____ must come over to my place," Sue said, "and

_____ can tell _____ all about it."

"Oh," _____ said, "_____ have a new dog called Sally and

_____ is a wonderful friend. _____ loves visitors."

"Bring _____ too," _____ said, "and _____ can all

go to the park if _____ like!"

B Write each of these **pronouns** in a sentence:

1. I   2. you   3. them   4. he   5. she   6. we   7. they

A **possessive pronoun** shows **possession** or **ownership**:

hers	his	ours	mine	theirs	yours

C Write each possessive **pronoun** from the box in a sentence.

Synonyms

Synonyms are words that have **similar meanings**.

These words are **synonyms** for **said**:

agreed	stated	told	ordered	boasted	mentioned
asked	suggested		announced		repeated
muttered	yelled	exclaimed		remarked	shouted

A Replace **said** with a **synonym** in each of these sentences:

1. "Does this train go to Liverpool?" she **said**.
2. "I stole the sweet," **said** the child.
3. "I'm a very good reader," he **said**.
4. "This is how it works!" she **said**.
5. "Here we go, here we go, here we go," they **said**.
6. "It's a secret!" he **said**.

B Replace **went** with a **synonym** in each of these sentences:

1. I **went** up the hill.
2. He **went** to school.
3. I **went** home.
4. We **went** to the shops.
5. The car **went** slowly.
6. He **went** across the river.
7. The cat **went** through the window.
8. Geeta **went** to Spain.
9. Ian **went** to see Karl.
10. The butterfly **went** from one flower to another.

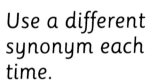

Use a different synonym each time.

Basic Rules of Grammar: Book 3

© Folens

Similes

Similes compare things.

Examples: The box was **as heavy as lead**.
Her hands were **as cold as ice**.

lion	lamb	bee	hare	owl
eel	horse	fox	kitten	wolf

A Complete these **similes** with an animal from the box:

1. as sly as a [ ]

2. as brave as a [ ]

3. as playful as a [ ]

4. as strong as a [ ]

5. as gentle as a [ ]

6. as hungry as a [ ]

7. as wise as an [ ]

8. as fast as a [ ]

9. as busy as a [ ]

10. as slippery as an [ ]

B Write five more **similes**.

Test 1

A Complete these **names** of countries.
Remember to begin each with a **capital letter**.

1. [   ]nce
2. [   ]zerland
3. [   ]tain
4. [   ]kistan
5. [   ]iland

B Write the **plurals** of these words:

1. lady
2. body
3. cry
4. tray
5. jelly

C Copy this story. Fill the spaces with **pronouns**:

Joe rang Emma one evening. [   ] had not spoken to [   ] for some time. "What have [   ] been up to since [   ] last met?" Joe asked [   ].

Emma replied, " [   ] have been on holiday with some friends. [   ] have all been to France for a week."

D Copy and complete these **similes**:

1. as cold as [   ]
2. as heavy as a [   ]
3. as slow as a [   ]
4. as dirty as a [   ]
5. as quiet as a [   ]

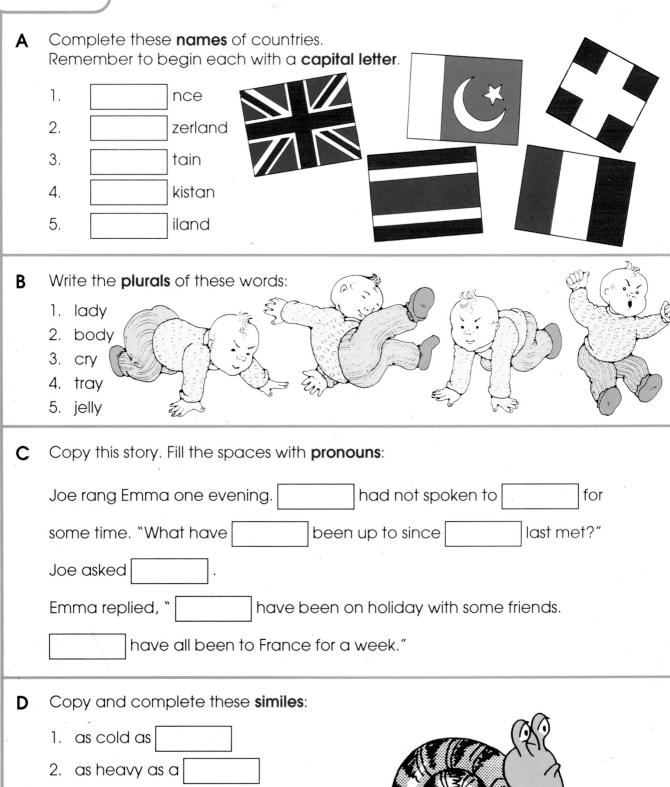

Basic Rules of Grammar: Book 3 © Folens

Adjectives

Adjectives are **describing** words.

Example: A **fat** cat met a **frightened** mouse on a **cold**, **dark** night.

A There are 14 **adjectives** in this story. List them.

The new girl came into the big school. She had silky black hair and dark eyes. She held her shiny blue bag tightly. In the noisy playground were strange, staring faces. Then a little girl came up and took her to a quiet room where she met her smiling, welcoming teacher.

B Write five **adjectives** to **describe** each of these:

1. a sunset
2. a rubbish dump
3. a summer day
4. a cat
5. a snake
6. a river
7. money
8. slime

C Write a noun that each group of **adjectives** could **describe**.

1. rusty, hard, heavy
2. ripe, yellow, tasty
3. eerie, dark, damp
4. round, flat, white
5. sweet, sticky, golden
6. fragile, transparent, hard
7. bouncy, round, red
8. blue, short, woollen, new

Adjectives

A sentence can often be made more interesting by adding an **adjective** or two.

Example: The girl drank the water.
The **thirsty** girl drank the **cool** water.

A   Re-write these sentences adding some **adjectives**.
The words in the box may help.

1. The teacher smiled at the children.

2. The dog barked at the moon.

3. The shark gnawed at the boat.

4. The car roared along the road.

5. The traveller stayed in the hotel.

6. The bus reversed into the van.

7. We ate strawberries and drank lemonade.

8. Two women carefully examined the glasses.

9. There were two chairs in the garden.

10. A swarm of bees settled on the branch.

wooden	happy
winding	silvery
timid	thoughtful
bloodthirsty	dilapidated
lonely	juicy
humming	freshly-painted
neglected	tired
distant	old
hungry	red
dusty	green
fragile	weary
vicious	smart
new	fizzy
shining	comfortable
buzzing	low
young	high

B   Change the sentences in **A** by using different **adjectives**.

Too nice

A There are more interesting words to describe things than **nice**.
Copy this story. Replace **nice** with a different word each time.

"It's a **nice** day. Let's go shopping", said Mum. "We can get you
some **nice** new clothes for Gran's party."
"Great," I muttered. "A **nice** dress, I expect."
"Oh, you look really **nice** in that. If you make your hair look **nice**
and put on some **nice** pretty shoes, you'll look ..."
"**Nice**!" I groaned.

B Draw some clothes. Write words on the clothes to describe them.

   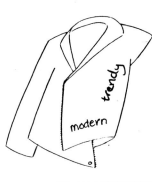

beautiful · strong · elegant · refined · trendy · modern · pretty

C Write a menu that includes all of these foods. Use at least two words to describe
each food. Do not use **nice**!

vegetable pizza

ice-cream delight

salad

baked potato

tuna with pasta

fruit salad

treacle pudding

cheese and biscuits

cheese roll

Description: Wanted!

A Look at this 'wanted' poster.
Write a television text report to
describe the criminal.
Use 40 to 50 words.
Underline the **adjectives**.

B Describe the getaway car
shown here.
Use 40 to 50 words.
Underline the **adjectives**.

C Draw this car. Compare it with a partner's drawing.
Re-write the description to make it clearer.

A dark blue Ford Orion saloon with a dented front bumper,
tinted windows and a wide yellow horizontal stripe on each side.
One door is dented. It has a sticker on the windscreen.
Registration number: Z26 918.

D 1. Find a photograph of a face. Describe it to a friend but
keep it hidden. Ask a friend to draw the face from
your description.

2. Draw a face that your friend describes.

3. Compare the drawings with the photographs. Re-draft and
improve your descriptions.

Descriptive sounds

Some words sound like the things that they describe.

crack	rustle	blare	jingle	hiss
sizzling	clang	popping	trickling	creaking

A Choose a **descriptive** sound from the box to complete the following:

1. The [＿＿＿] of a trumpet.

2. The [＿＿＿] of water.

3. The [＿＿＿] of a bell.

4. The [＿＿＿] of a whip.

5. The [＿＿＿] of a hinge.

6. The [＿＿＿] of steam.

7. The [＿＿＿] of coins.

8. The [＿＿＿] of corks.

9. The [＿＿＿] of leaves.

10. The [＿＿＿] of sausages.

B What might make these sounds?

1. rumble   2. crackle   3. howl   4. shriek   5. wail

C Write sentences about each of these.
Each sentence must have a **descriptive** sound.

1. owl
2. breaking glass
3. footsteps
4. voices
5. doorbell
6. birds
7. bees
8. mouse
9. machinery
10. traffic

Antonyms

Antonyms have **opposites**.

Example: **up** is the **antonym** of **down**.

A Re-write these sentences. Replace each word in red with its **antonym**.

1. The **fat** cat curled up under the **old** chair.

2. The curtains were made of a **thick**, **heavy** material.

3. She wore a **long** dress and a **large** hat.

4. The train travelled **slowly up** the slope.

5. We drank **hot** chocolate **late** one **night**.

6. "That is **difficult**," **shouted** Anna.

7. The ducks ate **stale** bread that **floated** in the **shallow** water.

8. She had a **sharp** pencil in her **left** hand.

9. "Please **close** the door," **shouted** Selina.

10. The **rich woman** lived in a **huge** house.

B Write the **antonyms** of:

1.	sweet	2.	hot
3.	bright	4.	pretty
5.	slow	6.	hard
7.	empty	8.	wet
9.	false	10.	poor
11.	fresh	12.	different
13.	heavy	14.	up
15.	noisy	16.	stop
17.	modern	18.	open
19.	idle	20.	in

Write sentences using four of these **antonyms**.

Words for pictures

A These pictures tell a story.
Choose the correct sentence to go with each picture.

The Football Match

He ran about the field
trying to show everyone
how good he was.

An ambulance came
and took him to
hospital.

They kept Tom in hospital
all night but he was able
to go home the next day.

He tried so hard to score
a goal that he ran into
the goalpost and
knocked himself out.

Tom had to be carried off
the football field.

Tom was very pleased
because he had been
chosen to play football
for the school.

See if you
can improve
the story.

B Re-write the story in your own words.

Test 2

A Copy and complete the **adjective** webs. One is done for you.

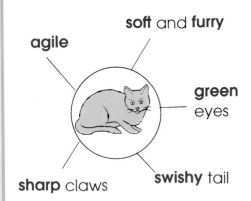

agile

soft and **furry**

green eyes

sharp claws

swishy tail

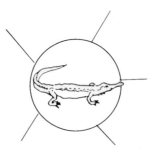

B Copy and complete these sentences with **adjectives**:

1. The ☐ man walked slowly down the ☐ road.

2. The ☐ monkeys played up in the ☐ trees.

3. The lady put her ☐ bag down. She was ☐ and ☐ .

4. The ☐ girl was so ☐ she forgot to collect her reading book.

C Re-write these sentences. Replace the words in red with their **antonyms**.

1. The bread was very **stale**.

2. The girl got all her spellings **correct**.

3. The fire spread **slowly** through the forest.

4. The knight suddenly **appeared**.

5. The boy **mended** his toy.

6. The baby's clothes looked very **dirty**.

Verbs

Verbs are **doing** words, or **being** words.

Example: It **was** sunny. We **ran** off and **played** outside.

A List the 12 **verbs** in this story:

They went on safari, but the van broke down!
Elephants chased them, snakes dropped on them,
tigers growled at them, giraffes stared at them,
cheetahs ran past them, rhinos pushed them and
alligators snapped at them. They screamed and
woke up. It was only a dream!

B Write one **verb** that means the same as these:

1. amble, stride, stroll
2. dash, race, speed
3. gobble, chew, devour
4. scribble, scrawl, inscribe
5. snooze, slumber, doze
6. flit, soar, flutter

C 1. List six things that you can do but animals cannot do.
All these words will be **verbs**.

Example: I can **read**.

2. Re-write this sentence four times, each time
using a different verb instead of **looked**:

He **looked** at the children.

Verb fun

A These **verbs** have been written in a way that shows their meanings:

stretch

wriggle   jump   climb

Which **verbs** could these be?
Each shape replaces a letter.

1.

2.

B Write these **verbs** in a way that shows their meanings:

1. explode   2. collapse   3. squirt

4. slide   5. grow   6. squash

C Some of the **verbs** in these silly sentences have lost a letter.
Write the sentences correctly.

1. The cocks **rowed** in the farmyard.

2. The two dogs were **baking**.

3. The feather **ticked** his feet.

4. The children will **pay** with the dolls.

5. **Hop** the onions into cubes.

6. We will **troll** in the countryside.

7. Please **utter** the bread.

8. He **ore** a pair of blue shoes.

Basic Rules of Grammar: Book 3
© Foler

Present, past, future

Verbs are **doing** words or **being** words. **Verbs** say what **is happening** or what **has happened**, or what **will happen**.
We call these the **present tense**, **past tense** or **future tense**.

We usually form the **past tense** by adding **d** or **ed**.

Example: race – race**d** jump – jump**ed**.

We usually form the **future tense** by putting **shall** or **will** in front of the **verb**.

Example: He **will** go away, I **shall** go fishing.

We use **shall** with **I** and **we**.
We use **will** with **she**, **he**, **it**, **you** and **they**.

A   Write these sentences in the **past tense**:

   1.   Two oil tankers collide in the fog.

   2.   She receives top marks in the exam.

   3.   I hand my money to the cashier.

   4.   He slips on the ice.

B   Write these sentences in the **future tense**:

   1.   In the tunnel your voice echoed.

   2.   I know we had a good time.

   3.   Sue helps you if you have any problems.

   4.   She says that she buys brown bread.

Some verbs are irregular when the **past tense** is formed.

Example: see – **saw**, grow – gr**ew**.

C   Write the **past tense** of these verbs:

bring	fly	give	go	win
write	swim	make	tell	ride

Adverbs

Adverbs tell us **more about verbs**. They **describe** what happens.

A   Find the **adverbs** in each of these examples:

Verb = to run	Verb = to snore	Verb = to shine	Verb = to blow
1. He ran quickly.	2. He snored loudly.	3. The sun shone brightly.	4. The wind blew strongly today.

B   Use this table to decode the **adverbs** in the story.
Copy the story. Underline the **adverbs**.

a	b	c	d	e	f	g	h	i	j	k	l	m	n	o	p	q	r	s	t	u	v	w	x	y	z
1	2	3	4	5	6	7	8	9	10	11	12	13	14	15	16	17	18	19	20	21	22	23	24	25	26

The burglar ☐ 19, 12, 15, 23, 12, 25 ☐ turned the key in the lock and

☐ 3, 1, 18, 5, 6, 21, 12, 12, 25 ☐ opened the door. He crept ☐ 17, 21, 9, 5, 20, 12, 25 ☐

into the house. A dog barked ☐ 14, 15, 9, 19, 9, 12, 25 ☐ and the burglar ran off

☐ 19, 13, 1, 18, 20, 12, 25 ☐ as fast as his legs would carry him. The noise woke all

the family. Father ran ☐ 17, 21, 9, 3, 11, 12, 25 ☐ down the stairs and out of the door

but he could not catch the burglar. The dog went on barking ☐ 12, 15, 21, 4, 12, 25 ☐

and would not stop but all the family smiled ☐ 8, 1, 16, 16, 9, 12, 25 ☐ at him.

He was a hero.

Adverbs

Many **adverbs** end in **ly**. Note the four common **adverbs** that do not follow this rule: **fast**, **well**, **soon** and **very**.

A Copy and complete this story with **adverbs**: ☆ ☆ ☆ ☆ ★ ★ ★

The Disco

In one house, Shelley and Tammy were ☐ looking forward to going

to the disco. They were getting ready ☐ . They were ☐

making choices – should it be skirts or leggings? Tammy ☐ tried on

leggings and Shelley ☐ chose a skirt. Meanwhile, Aaron and Matt

were setting off ☐ for the hall. The room ☐ filled up and the

lights went down ☐ . The music pounded ☐ and the

dancers began ☐ to go on to the floor. Aaron danced so ☐

that everyone stood still and clapped ☐ .

B Make these adjectives into **adverbs**:

1. angry   2. happy
3. sad   4. sleepy

C Write an **adverb** to go with each verb:

1. sing   2. fight   3. drive   4. write

D Write an **adverb** that starts with each of the following letters:

1. b ☐   2. h ☐   3. t ☐
4. m ☐   5. qu ☐   6. p ☐
7. a ☐   8. sl ☐   9. f ☐
10. g ☐   11. c ☐   12. d ☐

Apostrophes: contractions

The **apostrophe** is used to show where a **letter,** or **letters,** are **missed out**:

isn't	= is not		you're	= you are
can't	= cannot		don't	= do not

Words that are shortened in this way are called **contractions**.
Contractions are best used for conversation and informal
writing to friends and relatives. Use the long form for all other writing.

A Make a chart to match the long forms and
the **contractions** below:

contraction	long form
don't	do not

might have   don't   isn't   might've   man-of-war
I'd   do not   I would   mustn't
will not   can't   would not
won't   wouldn't   daren't   Simon is   dare not
is not   you'd   Simon's   you had
must not   we have   cannot   man o'war   we've

B This letter of complaint sounds too friendly. Re-write it.
Change the **contractions** to their longer forms.

Example: **I'm** becomes **I am**.

Dear Sir,

I'm writing to complain about the hole you've dug in the road just outside my house.
I can't get my car on to the drive. The workers start very early in the morning and
they're always making a noise.

I know the work has to be done, but you didn't write to let me know when it would
start. Also, you could have arranged for the workers to lay planks over the hole so
that I could get my car across.

Yours faithfully,

Apostrophes: ownership

This hat belongs to Peter = This is Peter**'s** hat.

In this sentence **'s** means **belongs to**.

A   Write who you think the object belongs to.
Remember the **apostrophe**.

Example: 1. The doctor**'s** stethoscope.

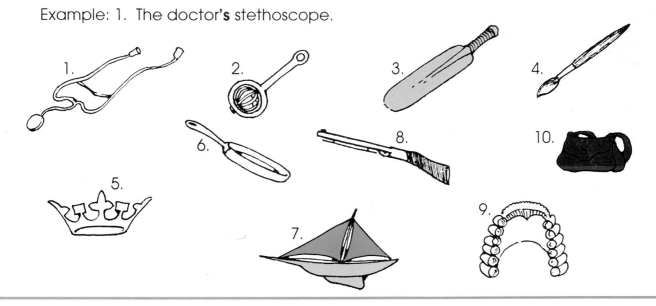

B   Copy these sentences adding **apostrophes**
where needed:

1. Alison borrowed Asmas pencils.
2. The children played in Mrs Fields garden.
3. The cat took the dogs bone.
4. The dentist examined the boys teeth.
5. The zoo keepers opened the lions cage.

> Remember. When
> adding **s** to make a
> plural you do not
> need an apostrophe.

A Re-write these sentences in both the **past** and **future tense**:

1. The bus is very late.
2. The children have sandwiches for lunch.
3. The police officer helps the lost child.
4. The waitress serves the hamburger to the hungry girl.
5. The birds fly away.
6. The window cleaner climbs the ladder.

B List the **adverbs** in this passage:

The cat crawled slowly behind the bushes. It watched hungrily as the birds busily pecked at worms in the garden. Suddenly it sprang. Fortunately the birds saw the cat leaping towards them and flew off nervously.

C Write out the long form of each of these **contractions**:

1. isn't
2. can't
3. I'm
4. doesn't
5. he's
6. wouldn't
7. they've
8. o'clock
9. don't
10. won't

D Put the missing **apostrophes** in these sentences:

1. Jim cleaned the horses hooves.
2. We played in Geetas garden.
3. Liams friends went with him to Peters house.
4. The schools library is full of new books.
5. The teachers pencil is on Jennys desk.
6. I cycled to the shops on Carlas new bike.

Capital letters

The most important uses of **capital letters** are to **begin sentences** and to **begin names of people** and **places**.

Examples: **O**nce upon a time there was ...
Simon, **D**oncaster

A   Copy and complete this passage using **capital letters** where they are needed:

it was only when the bus had started that trevor realised it was a barsley bus. that meant he could not get off until it stopped at the windmill estate. he would have to wait for a bus back and then wait for a kilnhurst bus. that meant he would be really late for school. mr wilkins would be furious.

B   Make the following lists:

1.   the names of six singers
2.   the names of six authors
3.   the names of six countries
4.   the names of six brands of sweets.

C   Copy and complete the chart with six more rows.

Names of people	Names of places	Days, months, special occasions	Brand names	Initials
Sarah	England	Monday	Ford	USA
Tony Adams	San Francisco	July	Reebok	RSPCA

Questions

World exclusive by The Young Reporter of the Year, Ida Story.

Today I interviewed a runaway princess. I asked her some questions.

A Below are some answers that the princess gave.
Write the **questions** Ida asked. Remember to use **question marks**.

1. My name is Snow White.

2. I lived in a castle with my father and stepmother.

3. I think she was jealous of me.

4. She told a huntsman to kill me.

5. I suppose he felt sorry for me.

6. I just wandered through the forest until I found a small cottage.

7. No, I'm not afraid. There are seven other people living there.

8. She might try to kill me.

B Write an interview with another story character.

Basic Rules of Grammar: Book 3 © Folens

Spoken words

These pictures tell a story.

Write what you think each person says in **speech marks**. Do it like this:

1. "Give me the bottle of sauce," Jill shouted.
   "No, I saw it first," Max replied.

Basic Rules of Grammar: Book 3

Spoken words

When we write a story in which people speak, we put the **words they say** into **speech marks** instead of a **speech bubble**.

"Hello," called the engineer.

"Hello. Nice day, isn't it?" James answered.

A Write these sentences correctly using **speech marks**:

1. Go home shouted James to Rover.

2. I'll write to you from Canada said Sue.

3. Is this Stilton cheese asked Jane. It looks more like Cheddar.

4. Who has eaten my lunch asked Bhavna.

5. Don't forget the tomatoes called Liam.

6. Peter said I think I'll go to the football match.

B Now write out this passage and put in the **speech marks**. Begin a new line when a different person speaks. Finish the story.

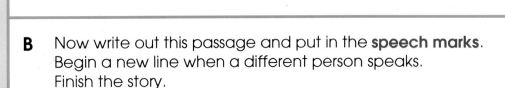

Now. Have you got everything Dad said. Yes we yelled from the back seat. Right then. Belts on and we're off. Wait Mum cried. I've shut the cat in. I'll have to go and let it out. Great sighed Dad. We stopped. Mum got out. Bet we will have forgotten something Fred muttered to me.

? or !

It is very easy to forget to use a **question mark** or **exclamation mark**.

A **question mark** is used **after a question**.

Example: "What time is it?".

An **exclamation mark** is used to show **surprise**, **delight** or when someone **shouts**.

Example: "How strange!", "What a nice day!", "Help!".

A   Draw speech bubbles for each of the pictures and write
     what each character is saying.
     Use **question marks** or **exclamation marks** at the end of
     each speech.

B   Sketch your own scenes. Ask a partner to fill in the speech bubbles.

Dialogue

Speech marks, or **inverted commas**, are used **before** and **after** the **words which are actually spoken**.

A new line is used every time the speaker changes. This makes it clearer for the reader.

"Knock, Knock."
"Who's there?"
"Alison."
"Alison who?"
"Alison to the radio."

`Knock, Knock' jokes are short conversations that end in a funny punch line.

Full stops, question marks, exclamation marks and **commas** are inside the **speech marks**:

"Alison who?"
not
"Alison who"?

A Punctuate these `Knock, Knock' jokes:

Knock Knock
Who's there
Olive
Olive who
Olive here so let me in

Knock Knock
Who's there
Me
Me who
Is there a cat around

Knock Knock
Who's there
Arfer
Arfer who
Arfer got

Knock Knock
Who's there
Frank
Frank who
Frankenstein

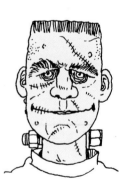

B Do you know more `Knock, Knock' jokes?
Write them down and punctuate them.

Basic Rules of Grammar: Book 3

© Folens

Rhyme time

Rhyming words have the **same final sound**.

What do you call an angry father?

A mad dad!

A   Finish these answers so that they **rhyme**:

1.	Absolutely correct.	→ quite	**right**
2.	Cut two times.	→ slice	
3.	A plate of sea food.	→ fish	
4.	An angry employer.	→ cross	
5.	An overweight rodent.	→ fat	
6.	Blond curls.	→ fair	
7.	To tear open a metal fastener.	→ rip	
8.	Huge hog.	→ big	
9.	Expensive ale.	→ dear	
10.	A metal container.	→ tin	
11.	Police chief.	→ top	
12.	Goldilocks sat in them.	→ bears'	
13.	Recipe collection.	→ cook	
14.	To blow a wind instrument.	→ toot	
15.	Sprain your forearm.	→ twist	

B   Think of some examples of your own.

Basic Rules of Grammar: Book 3

Test 4

A Copy and complete this passage using **capital letters** where they are needed:

kings cross station was very busy when katie and claire arrived. this was because it was christmas eve and lots of people were going away for the holidays. katie and claire were going to edinburgh to visit katie's aunt philippa who had invited them to stay until the new year.

B Here are the answers to some **questions**. Write the **questions**.

1. I like apple pie and custard best.
2. It looks as if it will rain.
3. It's made of wood, I think.
4. I've written it in my note book.
5. No I do not like cheese.
6. There are seven.
7. We will go on Saturday.
8. It will be on 14th July.
9. They live in Manchester.

C Describe what is happening in the pictures. Write what the characters are saying in **speech marks**. Remember to include any **question marks** and **exclamation marks** that have been missed.

D Copy this table of **rhyming** words. Add six words to each column.

wear	table	high	tough
bear			

Homophones

Homophones are words that sound the same, but they are **spelled differently** and they **mean different things**.

I **won** the race.   I have **one** mouth.

A   One word in each pair of **homophones** has been put into a sentence.
Write sentences using the other word in each pair. The pictures will help you.

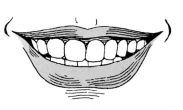
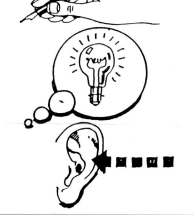

1. | by / buy | I sat by my friend.

2. | meet / meat | I ran to meet my Gran.

3. | our / hour | This is our school.

4. | right / write | This is my right hand.

5. | new / knew | My bag is new.

6. | here / hear | Here is the right shop.

B   List six more **homophones**. Draw pictures beside each one to help you remember which word is which. Here are some to start you off: see and sea, rode and road, red and read, their and they're.

Commonly confused words

Copy the story of Goldilocks and the Three Bears.
Choose the correct words.

Once upon a time **an/a** little girl called Goldilocks went for a walk in the **wood/would**. She did not **know/no** that there were dangerous animals in the **wood/would**.

Suddenly she came upon a little house.

"**I/me** wonder who lives **here/hear**," she thought. "**There/their** doesn't seem to be anybody about."

She knocked on the door and walked in. In front **of/off** her **were/where** three bowls of steaming porridge.

She tasted the first one and screamed, "This porridge is **too/to** hot **to/too** eat!"

There were **two/to** bowls left so she tasted another **won/one**.

"Yuk! This porridge is **too/to/two** sweet!" she shouted.

There **were/was** one bowl left so she tasted that one.

"Mmm! This porridge is just **write/right**!" she said.

Goldilocks was so tired that she fell asleep in a small bed. She did not know that the Three **Bears/Bares** who lived **there/their** had returned from their walk in the woods.

Father Bear shouted, "Who **are/is** sleeping in Baby Bear's bed?"

Mother Bear shouted, "Who **do/does** she think she is!"

Goldilocks jumped up and ran away.

Baby Bear shouted after her, "Next time **bye/buy** your own porridge!"

Poor Goldilocks! She **done/did** not **no/know** what she had **did/done** wrong!

Basic Rules of Grammar: Book 3

Conjunctions

A **conjunction** is a word used to **join small sentences together**.

Example: We have missed the bus **so** we will have to walk.

A   Copy this story and underline the **conjunctions**:

We could not get into the house because we had left the keys on the
hall table. We would have to wait outside in the garden until my brother
came home at six o'clock. Chris thought he could climb in through the
bedroom window although this was not a good plan because we didn't
have a long enough ladder.

B   Copy and complete the following sentences using the **conjunctions** in the box:

1. We went to the zoo [   ] saw some elephants.
2. Lucy was wet [   ] she had forgotten her umbrella.
3. I like coffee [   ] I would prefer tea.
4. Greg put on his suit [   ] he went to work.
5. You cannot go in the sea [   ] you can swim.

> before
> and
> because
> unless
> but

C   Copy this story and fill the gaps with **conjunctions**:

We were locked out [   ] we had lost our keys.
Mum was at Grandma's house [   ] she would
come home early [   ] we could phone her
and let her know. We could not use our phone [   ] Mrs. Jones
next door was at home. We went to ask if we could call Mum from
her house. We rang the bell [   ] Mrs Jones called out telling us
to wait [   ] she was having a bath. We were waiting on the
doorstep [   ] Dad came home early. He was not very pleased
[   ] moaned at us, " [   ] you start looking after your
things better you will have to go to Gran's every night."

Alphabet quiz

A Read the clues. Write the words by choosing the endings from the box.

1. Break into small pieces   sm [   ] .

2. A fish with sharp teeth   sh [   ] .

3. The bone of your head   sk [   ] .

4. Shoes worn indoors   sl [   ] .

5. Seat on a horse's back   sa [   ] .

6. For digging with   sp [   ] .

7. A four-sided shape   sq [   ] .

8. Quiet   si [   ] .

9. Frozen rain   sn [   ] .

10. Wear it for warmth   sc [   ] .

_ ddle
_ ull
_ ow
_ arf
_ ash
_ uare
_ ade
_ ippers
_ lent
_ ark

B Write the words in **A** in **alphabetical order**.

C These children have agreed to bat in **alphabetical order** of first names.

1. Write the order in which they will bat.

2. Write the order in which they would bat if they used surnames.

Gordon Richards

Helen Ramsbottom

Brian Riley

Karen Remmington

Lorenna Rinaldi

Ian Reid

Anna Rice

Prepositions

Prepositions show how one word **relates** to another.

Examples: **in** the bottle, **out of** the bottle, **down** the throat.

A Copy this story. Fill the gaps with **prepositions**.

The Spectacular Stunts

The brave woman crashed [____] the ceiling [____] a strong rope. There was a crystal [____] the ground [____] her. It had strange writing [____] it. Suddenly, sharp spikes popped [____] of the walls and began to dig [____] her. She raced [____] two rocks, grabbed the crystal and charged [____] the stairs. A boulder came [____] her and she flattened herself [____] the rock wall. The boulder went [____] and she was safe.

B Write a **preposition** that starts with each of the following letters:

1. b [____]   2. o [____]   3. a [____]

4. t [____]   5. f [____]   6. u [____]

7. n [____]   8. w [____]   9. i [____]

C Copy and complete these sentences. Underline the **prepositions**.

1. I will complain about [____].

2. He suffers from [____].

3. She is guilty of [____].

4. Jane agreed with [____].

5. Manchester is different from [____].

Test 5

A Decide which is the correct word to use in each sentence:

1. "**Weight/wait** here," the girl whispered.

2. I had to **write/right** a thank you letter for my present.

3. Can you **here/hear** that noise?

4. It will take an **our/hour** to walk home.

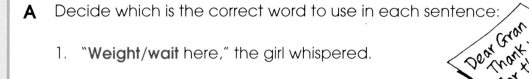

B Copy this story and fill the gaps with **conjunctions**:

The bus was late [   ] we decided to walk home. We had not gone far

[   ] we heard a strange noise. We stopped to look [   ] we thought

someone was hurt. I did not want to look [   ] I was frightened

[   ] the others made me. I walked over [   ] looked in

the ditch.

C Write each set of words in **alphabetical order**:

1.	slime	sweet	space	sandwich	sentry
2.	single	stop	snip	shout	son
3.	sun	scrub	squeeze	sadly	ship

D Copy these sentences and underline the **prepositions**:

1. I tied a ribbon around the parcel.

2. There is a tunnel under the English Channel.

3. There were plants along the edge of the path.

4. Above our seats was a shelf for luggage.

5. The children played beside the lake.

Prefixes

Prefixes go before some words to change their meanings.
Dis is a prefix that means **apart** or **not**.

Example: obey – **dis**obey.

A Put the **prefix dis** before each of these words:

1.	appear	2.	able
3.	arm	4.	agrees
5.	band	6.	obey
7.	covered	8.	count
9.	charged	10.	allowed
11.	close	12.	trust

B Copy these sentences replacing the words in red with one word from your list in **A**.

1. The parent **does not agree** with what the child says.

2. The police officer had to **take the weapon from** the gunman.

3. The referee **did not allow** the goal.

4. The pupil will **refuse to obey** the teacher.

5. Sherlock Holmes **found out** who committed the crime.

C Write a word starting with **dis** that has the same meaning as these:

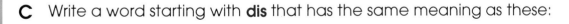

1. not allow
2. break up a group
3. not honest
4. remove infection or germs
5. dig up something buried
6. hate
7. take apart
8. send a letter or parcel
9. argue
10. share out.

USE YOUR DICTIONARY

Suffixes

Suffixes are added to the ends of some words.
Ful is a **suffix** that means **full of**.

Some words are made by adding **ful** to a **root** word.

Example: the **root** word of **colourful** is **colour**.

A Copy the words in these sentences that have **suffixes**.
Underline the **root** words.

1. You should be careful when using sharp knives.
2. A spoonful of sugar makes the medicine go down.
3. The forgetful student sat his examinations with dreadful results.
4. The beautiful girl was grateful for the flowers.
5. There is only a handful left in the bag.
6. The strange sounds made us fearful.
7. Jane was tearful as she told me her sad news.
8. Jack had a bucketful of water.
9. We sat in a peaceful corner.
10. Graceful swans glided along the river.
11. Green is a restful colour.

B Add **ful** to the following words and write the new words.
Remember words ending in **y** change **y** to **i**.

1. success – successful
2. event –
3. master –
4. plenty –
5. harm –
6. sorrow –
7. beauty –
8. care –
9. joy –
10. bounty –
11. peace –
12. cheer –
13. colour –
14. sin –
15. right –
16. help –
17. pity –
18. dread –
19. hand –
20. tear –
21. mourn –
22. forget –
23. use –
24. arm –

Syllabication

When a **two-syllable** word ends in **y**, the **y** says **ee**.
The **y** uses the consonant before it to make the last **syllable**.

Copy each word.
Draw a line between the **syllables**, for example seven/ty, fus/sy.

1. silly	2. rusty	3. sixty
4. misty	5. jolly	6. fluffy
7. angry	8. jelly	9. happy
10. crazy	11. chilly	12. nappy
13. handy	14. friendly	15. glossy
16. cosy	17. candy	18. rainy
19. messy	20. ugly	21. clumsy
22. dolly	23. fifty	24. grassy

Instructions

A Read this **information**:

Here is how I make a good cup of tea. The first thing I do is to fill the kettle with water and put it on to boil. While I am waiting for the water to boil, I get the teapot out and put some milk into the cup. When the water boils, I pour a little into the teapot to warm it. When the pot is warm, I tip the water away and put in some tea leaves or teabags. Next I pour some boiling water into the teapot. I usually wait a minute or two to let the tea get a little stronger then I pour some into the cup.

Use the information to help you write a list of **instructions** about how to make a cup of tea.

Copy and continue this chart.

1. Fill the kettle with water.
2.

B What are these **instructions** for?

1.
Collect three wires, a battery, bulb, bulb holder and screwdriver.
Screw a bulb into a holder.
Attach a wire to each screw.
Fasten one wire to the battery.
Join the other wire to a switch.
Attach the third wire to the switch.
Join this to the battery.

2.
Set the oven at 220°C.
Rub together the flour, sugar and margarine.
Add milk.
Shape the dough in to a ball.
Roll it out about 2cm thick.
Cut the dough into rounds.
Bake them on a greased baking tray for 20 minutes.

C Write **instruction charts** for these:

1. Loading a computer programme.
2. Making a cheese sandwich.
3. Setting a video recorder.

Basic Rules of Grammar: Book 3 © Folens

Sequence

A Write a list of all the places Dr Jones passed on the way to the Temple. Put them in the right order. Remember the commas.

Start

Erupting volcano

Wild bear's cave

Rope bridge across ravine

Snake infested jungle

Crocodile river

Lion trap

Deserted village

Alligator swamp

Strange statues

Temple of the Moon

B Pick five of the places Dr Jones visited. Write the sort of things you think she saw and did at each one.

Basic Rules of Grammar: Book 3

Proofreading

A   Copy and correct this story. Look for **spelling mistakes** and missing **full stops**, **capital letters** and **apostrophes**.

On saterday im gowing to get my ears pierced My frend hannah

said she will cume wiv me becuase im two scared to go on my own

I fink it will hurt and if I sea blod I will bee sick

My friend lucy has had her ears dun and sed she didnt fel a thing

The earings I like best are the very big long ones

Sum of my frends have to or free earings in each ear

How many mistakes did you find?

B   1.   Copy and correct this story. Look for **spelling mistakes** and missing **punctuation**.

Sometime latter, the kings musitiun brok his harp He searched evrywere for the wood of a willo tree to make a new harp at last he found a willow treee by a streem He cut down the tree and made a beutiful harp from the soft would

That knight there was a big feest in Knig larrys palace All the nobles and lords were in the great hall The king ordered his harper to play sum musik for his guests But when the harper plucked the strings, the harp began to sing loudly:

"king larry has the hears of a horse...the ears of a horse"

There was sylence int he great hal

2.   Continue the story.
Proofread and correct your new
part of the story.
Ask a friend to proofread it.

Basic Rules of Grammar: Book 3   © Folens

Missing words: making sense

A Work with a partner. Read the passage below.

Choose a word from the box to go in each space.

watching	able	small	astronaut	giant	seen	large
believe	world	moon	gravity	first	step	

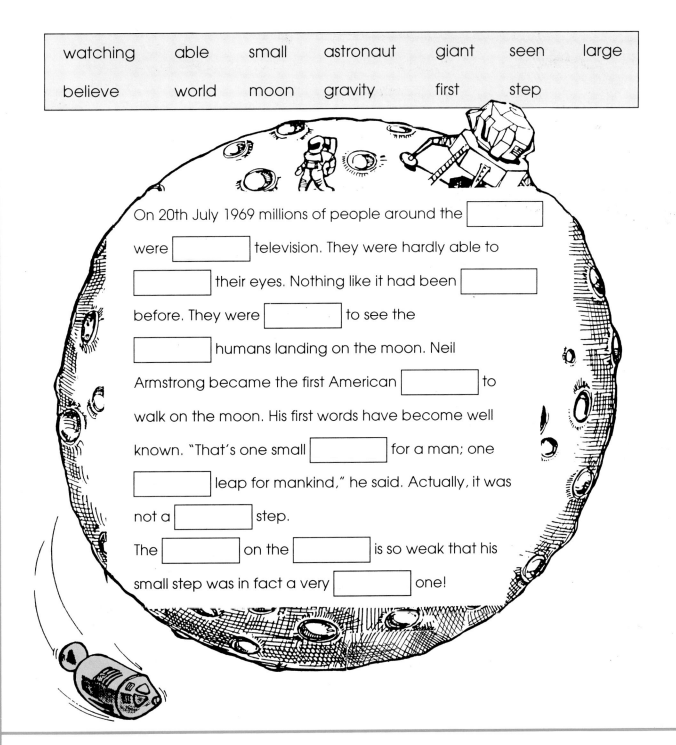

On 20th July 1969 millions of people around the ☐

were ☐ television. They were hardly able to

☐ their eyes. Nothing like it had been ☐

before. They were ☐ to see the

☐ humans landing on the moon. Neil

Armstrong became the first American ☐ to

walk on the moon. His first words have become well

known. "That's one small ☐ for a man; one

☐ leap for mankind," he said. Actually, it was

not a ☐ step.

The ☐ on the ☐ is so weak that his

small step was in fact a very ☐ one!

B 1. Read the passage again. Do the words you have chosen
make sense? Is there just one correct answer for each word?

Test 6

A Choose the **prefix re** or **dis** to go in front of each word.
Write the complete words.

1. ☐ appear   2. ☐ sist

3. ☐ peat   4. ☐ miss

5. ☐ sume   6. ☐ obey

7. ☐ agree   8. ☐ lease

B Take the **suffix ful** off each word. Write the **root** word you are left with.

1. harmful
2. careful
3. helpful
4. peaceful
5. wonderful

C Copy these words and split them into two **syllables**:

| plenty | milky | ready | risky | sixty |
| runny | shiny | forty | lovely | twenty |

D Write a sentence listing your five favourite
television programmes.

Don't forget
the commas.

E This story has some spelling and punctuation mistakes.
Proofread it and write it correctly.

larst weak my frend and I whent shoping the shops where verry bizzy
so we didint stay long I brout a pear of brite orınge trowsers but my
mum fort thay wear terrable